This book belongs to:

_____

who absolutely loves her fro!

2

To all of you beautiful little girls
out there and your super funky,
fabulous fros!

Sundays are my most favourite day because I get to change my hair,

every morning I jump out of bed and rush right down the stairs.

Mum has to wash my hair so it's clean
before we make a start,
she shampoos and conditions it, I really like this part.

She squeezes all the water out then I sit between her knees,

she dries my hair and moisturises it, then it's over to me.

"What style would you like today, Kemi?"
Mummy asks me.
I "umm" and "ahh" until I decide what it's going to be.

Sometimes I have bouncy braids...

...and sometimes I have twists.

Sometimes I have canerows with beads on the end like this!

Sometimes I wear a ponytail...

...or a ballerina bun.

Maybe one day I'll try dancing dreadlocks,
they look really fun!

Today I think I'm going to wear
my awesome afro hair,

every time I move you'll see it swaying everywhere.

Whenever we're done I run to take a look in the mirror,

Mummy makes me twirl around and pose for a picture.

She says I'm lucky to have my hair, I can do whatever I like...

...whether it's big or small or short or long it'll always look really nice.

Mum says, "Your hair is special and it's a part of who you are,

no matter the length or curl or colour, you'll always be a star.

You have to make sure you take care of it and then you'll be able to explore,

all of these super pretty styles
and a million trillion more".

It doesn't matter what people say or what they think they know,

you have to be sure you love yourself and always...

...Love Thy Fro!

What does your fro look like?

What do you love about your fro?

I love my fro because...